The Wheels on the Bus

and Other Transportation Songs

Illustrated by Dick Witt

Cartwheel
B·O·O·K·S™

SCHOLASTIC INC.

New York   Toronto   London   Auckland   Sydney

For Emily, Jonathon, and Cecilia
—D.W.

ISBN 0-590-47276-3

12 11 10 9 8 7 6 5   0 1 2/0

Printed in the U.S.A.   24

First Scholastic printing, May 1994

Contents

Daisy, Daisy

Daisy, Daisy,
Give me your answer, do.
I'm half crazy,
All for the love of you.

It won't be a stylish marriage.
I can't afford a carriage.

But you'll look sweet
Upon the seat
Of a bicycle built for two.

Down by the Station

Down by the station,
Early in the morning,
See the little puffer-bellies
All in a row.

I can see the engineer
Pull a little lever.
Puff! Puff! Toot! Toot!
Off they go!

I've Been Working on the Railroad

I've been working on the railroad
All the livelong day.
I've been working on the railroad
Just to pass the time away.

9

Can't you hear the whistle blowing?
Rise up so early in the morn.
Can't you hear the captain shouting,
"Dinah blow your horn."

Dinah won't you blow,
Dinah won't you blow,
Dinah won't you blow your horn?

Dinah won't you blow,
Dinah won't you blow,
Dinah won't you blow your horn?

Someone's in the kitchen with Dinah.
Someone's in the kitchen, I know.
Someone's in the kitchen with Dinah,
Strumming on the old banjo.

Fee fi fiddlee-i-o,
Fee fi fiddlee-i-o-o-o-o,
Fee fi fiddlee-i-o,
Strumming on the old banjo.

DINAH'S
DAY CARE

13

Sally Go Round the Sun

Sally go round the sun.
Sally go round the moon.

Sally go round the chimney top,
Every afternoon.

14

She'll Be Comin' Round the Mountain

She'll be comin' round the mountain
When she comes.
She'll be comin' round the mountain
When she comes.

She'll be comin' round the mountain,
She'll be comin' round the mountain,
She'll be comin' round the mountain
When she comes.

17

She'll be driving six white horses
When she comes.
She'll be driving six white horses
When she comes.

She'll be driving six white horses,
She'll be driving six white horses,
She'll be driving six white horses
When she comes.

Oh, we'll all go out to greet her
When she comes.
Oh, we'll all go out to greet her
When she comes.

Oh, we'll all go out to greet her,
Oh, we'll all go out to greet her,
Oh, we'll all go out to greet her
When she comes.

Yankee Doodle

Yankee Doodle went to town,
Riding on a pony;
He stuck a feather in his cap
And called it macaroni.

Ride a Cockhorse

Ride a cockhorse to Banbury Cross,
To see a fine lady upon a white horse;
Rings on her fingers and bells on her toes,
She shall have music wherever she goes.

Row, Row, Row Your Boat

Row, row, row your boat,
Gently down the stream.
Merrily, merrily,
Merrily, merrily,
Life is but a dream.

Row, row, row your boat,
Gently down the stream.
Merrily, merrily,
Merrily, merrily,
Life is but a dream.

Row, row, row your boat,
Gently down the stream.
Merrily, merrily,
Merrily, merrily,
Life is but a dream.

Row, row, row your boat,
Gently down the stream.
Merrily, merrily,
Merrily, merrily,
Life is but a dream.

The Wheels on the Bus

The wheels on the bus go round and round,
Round and round, round and round.
The wheels on the bus go round and round
All through the town.

The wipers on the bus go swish swish swish,
Swish swish swish, swish swish swish.
The wipers on the bus go swish swish swish
All through the town.

The doors on the bus go open and shut,
Open and shut, open and shut.
The doors on the bus go open and shut
All through the town.

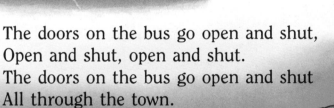

The driver on the bus says, "Move on back!
Move on back! Move on back!"
The driver on the bus says, "Move on back!"
All through the town.

The people on the bus go bumpity bump,
Bumpity bump, bumpity bump.
The people on the bus go bumpity bump
All through the town.

The horn on the bus goes beep beep beep,
Beep beep beep, beep beep beep.
The horn on the bus goes beep beep beep
All through the town.

The babies on the bus go, "Wah wah wah!
Wah wah wah! Wah wah wah!"
The babies on the bus go, "Wah wah wah!"
All through the town.

The parents on the bus say, "Shh shh shh!
Shh shh shh! Shh shh shh!"
The parents on the bus say, "Shh shh shh!"
All through the town.

The wheels on the bus go round and round,
Round and round, round and round.
The wheels on the bus go round and round
All through the town.